M000250980

THE SOLAR SYSTEM
Space and Beyond Series

• •

Written by Charlene Homer

GRADES 5 - 8
Reading Levels 3 - 4

Classroom Complete Press
P.O. Box 19729
San Diego, CA 92159
Tel: 1-800-663-3609 / Fax: 1-800-663-3608
Email: service@classroomcompletepress.com

www.classroomcompletepress.com

ISBN-13: 978-1-55319-315-9
ISBN-10: 1-55319-315-6

© 2007

© CLASSROOM COMPLETE PRESS

Critical Thinking Skills

The Solar System

Skills For Critical Thinking	Reading Comprehension							Hands-on Activities
	Section 1	Section 2	Section 3	Section 4	Section 5	Section 6	Section 7	
LEVEL 1 Knowledge								
• List Details/Facts	✓	✓	✓	✓	✓	✓	✓	✓
• Recall Information	✓	✓	✓	✓	✓	✓	✓	
• Match Vocab. to Definitions	✓	✓		✓	✓		✓	
• Define Vocabulary	✓		✓	✓			✓	
• Label Diagrams				✓				
• Recognize Validity (T/F)	✓	✓	✓		✓			
LEVEL 2 Comprehension								
• Demonstrate Understanding	✓		✓	✓		✓	✓	✓
• Explain Scientific Causation		✓	✓			✓		
• Rephrasing Vocab. Meaning		✓	✓	✓				
• Describe	✓				✓		✓	✓
• Classify into Scientific Groups					✓	✓		
LEVEL 3 Application								
• Application to Own Life	✓		✓			✓	✓	✓
• Model Scientific Process					✓			
• Organize and Classify Facts	✓			✓				
• Utilize Alternative Research Tools	✓	✓			✓		✓	
LEVEL 4 Analysis								
• Distinguish Roles/Meanings		✓			✓			
• Make Inferences	✓		✓		✓	✓		✓
• Draw Conclusions Based on Facts Provided	✓		✓		✓		✓	✓
• Classify Based on Facts Researched		✓	✓			✓		
LEVEL 5 Synthesis								
• Compile Research Information	✓	✓		✓	✓			
• Design and Application	✓		✓	✓			✓	
• Create and Construct	✓		✓			✓	✓	✓
• Imagine Self in Scientific Role		✓		✓		✓	✓	
LEVEL 6 Evaluation								
• State and Defend an Opinion		✓		✓		✓		
• Justify Choices for Research & Topics	✓	✓	✓	✓	✓		✓	
• Defend Selections and Reasoning			✓					✓

Based on Bloom's Taxonomy

The Solar System CC451

Contents

FREE! 6 Bonus Activities!

3 EASY STEPS to receive your 6 Bonus Activities!
- Go to our website:
  www.classroomcompletepress.com\bonus
- Click on item **CC4512 – The Solar System**
- Enter pass code **CC4512D**

Assessment Rubric

The Solar System

Student's Name: _____ Assignment: _____ Level: _____

	Level 1	Level 2	Level 3	Level 4
Understanding Concepts	Demonstrates a limited understanding of concepts. Requires teacher intervention.	Demonstrates a basic understanding of the concepts.	Demonstrates a good understanding of the concepts.	Demonstrates a thorough understanding of the concepts.
Response to the Text	Expresses responses to the text with limited effectiveness, inconsistently supported with proof from the text.	Expresses responses to the text with some effectiveness, supported with some proof from the text.	Expresses responses to the text with appropriate skills, supported with appropriate proof.	Expresses thorough and complete responses to the text, supported by concise and effective proof from the text.
Analysis & Application of Concepts	Interprets and applies various concepts in the text with few, unrelated details and incorrect analysis.	Interprets and applies various concepts in the text with some detail, but with some inconsistent analysis.	Interprets and applies various concepts in the text with appropriate detail and analysis.	Effectively interprets and applies various concepts in the text with consistent, clear, and effective detail and analysis.

STRENGTHS:

WEAKNESSES:

NEXT STEPS:

Teacher Guide

Our resource has been created for ease of use by both TEACHERS and STUDENTS alike.

Introduction

This resource provides ready-to-use information and activities for remedial students in grades five to eight. Written to grade using simplified language and vocabulary, science concepts are presented in a way that makes them more accessible to students and easier to understand. Comprised of reading passages, student activities and mini posters, our resource can be used effectively for whole-class, small group and independent work.

How Is Our Resource Organized?

STUDENT HANDOUTS

Reading passages and **activities** (*in the form of reproducible worksheets*) make up the majority of our resource. The reading passages present important grade-appropriate information and concepts related to the topic. Embedded in each passage are one or more questions that ensure students understand what they have read.

For each reading passage there are BEFORE YOU READ activities and AFTER YOU READ activities.

- The BEFORE YOU READ activities prepare students for reading by setting a purpose for reading. They stimulate background knowledge and experience, and guide students to make connections between what they know and what they will learn. Important concepts and vocabulary are also presented.

- The AFTER YOU READ activities check students' comprehension of the concepts presented in the reading passage and extend their learning. Students are asked to give thoughtful consideration of the reading passage through creative and evaluative short-answer questions, research, and extension activities.

Hands-on activities are included to further develop students' thinking skills and understanding of the concepts. The **Assessment Rubric** (*page 4*) is a useful tool for evaluating students' responses to many of the activities in our resource. The **Comprehension Quiz** (*page 48*) can be used for either a follow-up review or assessment at the completion of the unit.

PICTURE CUES

Our resource contains three main types of pages, each with a different purpose and use. A **Picture Cue** at the top of each page shows, at a glance, what the page is for.

🍎 **Teacher Guide**
- Information and tools for the teacher

✏️ **Student Handout**
- Reproducible worksheets and activities

EZ✓ **Easy Marking™ Answer Key**
- Answers for student activities

EASY MARKING™ ANSWER KEY
Marking students' worksheets is fast and easy with this **Answer Key**. Answers are listed in columns – just line up the column with its corresponding worksheet, as shown, and see how every question matches up with its answer!

Every question matches up with its answer!

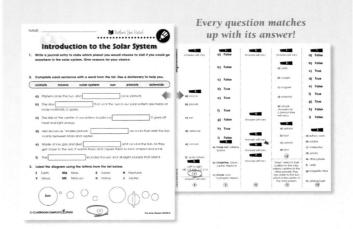

Bloom's Taxonomy

Our resource is an effective tool for any SCIENCE PROGRAM.

Bloom's Taxonomy* for Reading Comprehension

The activities in our resource engage and build the full range of thinking skills that are essential for students' reading comprehension and understanding of important **science concepts**. Based on the six levels of thinking in Bloom's Taxonomy, and using language at a remedial level, information and questions are given that challenge students to not only recall what they have read, but move beyond this to understand the text and concepts through higher-order thinking. By using higher-order skills of application, analysis, synthesis and evaluation, students become active readers, drawing more meaning from the text, attaining a greater understanding of concepts, and applying and extending their learning in more sophisticated ways.

Our resource, therefore, is an effective tool for any **Science** program. Whether it is used in whole or in part, or adapted to meet individual student needs, our resource provides teachers with essential information and questions to ask, inspiring students' interest, creativity, and promoting meaningful learning.

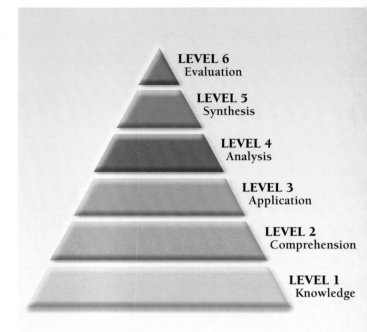

**BLOOM'S TAXONOMY:
6 LEVELS OF THINKING**

Bloom's Taxonomy is a widely used tool by educators for classifying learning objectives, and is based on the work of Benjamin Bloom.

Vocabulary

comet	solar system	asteroid	asteroid belt	orbit
hydrogen	helium	satellite	atmosphere	meteor
meteorite	sulfuric acid	magnetic field	gravity	nitrogen
oxygen	rotate	evidence	exploration	rover
channels	astronaut	dwarf	geyser	zone
methane	lunar	phase	cycle	reflect
crater	eclipse	illuminated	waxing	waning
gibbous	crescent	astronomer	navigate	constellation
telescope	light years	nebula	supernova	galaxy
universe	north star	black hole	shooting star	particles
asterism	debris	impact		

NAME: _____

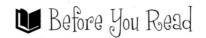 Before You Read

Introduction to the Solar System

1. **Write a journal entry to state which planet you would choose to visit if you could go anywhere in the solar system. Give reasons for your choice.**

2. **Complete each sentence with a word from the list. Use a dictionary to help you.**

comets	moons	solar system	sun	planets	asteroids

a) Planets circle the Sun, and [   ] circle planets.

b) The eight [   ] that orbit the Sun in our solar system are made of rocky materials or gases.

c) The star at the center of our system is called a [   ]. It gives off heat and light energy.

d) Also known as "smaller planets", [   ] are rocks that orbit the Sun mainly between Mars and Jupiter.

e) Made of ice, gas and dust, [   ] orbit around the Sun. As they get closer to the Sun, it warms them and causes them to form a head and a tail.

f) The [   ] includes the sun and all eight planets that orbit it.

3. **Label the diagram using the letters from the list below.**

E	Earth	**MA**	Mars	**S**	Saturn	**N**	Neptune
V	Venus	**ME**	Mercury	**U**	Uranus	**J**	Jupiter

    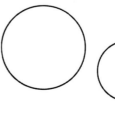 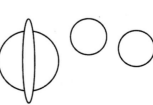

Sun

Introduction: The Solar System

Did you know that people once believed that Earth was the center of the solar system? They thought that all of the planets and the Sun revolved around us! Now we know that our solar system has eight planets that travel around the Sun. The planets travel in circular paths called **orbits.** The planets are divided into **inner planets** and **outer planets.** The first four planets, Mercury, Venus, Earth and Mars, are the inner planets. Then, Jupiter, Saturn, Uranus and Neptune are the outer planets. Pluto lost its planetary status in 2006.

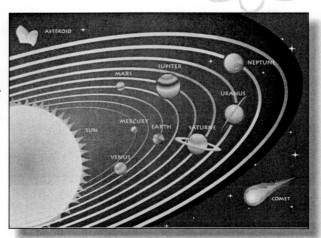

The inner and outer planets have a row of asteroids in between them. It is called an **asteroid belt.** Asteroids are pieces of space rock that orbit around the Sun. Scientists think that asteroids are like "space trash", leftover garbage from when the planets were first formed.

Make a list of all of the things in our solar system that you have read about so far.

_____

_____

The eight planets in our solar system are made of either rocky materials or gases. Mercury, Venus, Earth and Mars are the **rocky planets.** They are smaller than planets made of gas. They are also heavier and move more slowly. They have no **rings** around them. The rocky planets have few **moons.** The former planet, Pluto, is also rocky, has no rings and has few moons around it.

Jupiter, Saturn, Uranus and Neptune are the **gas planets.** They are made of gases called **hydrogen** and **helium.** These big planets are often called the **"Gas Giants".** They are lighter than the rocky planets and move faster. Most of these planets have many moons. Did you know that Jupiter has sixty-three moons? All of the gas planets also have rings around them, but Saturn's rings are most well known. You have probably seen pictures of the rings around Saturn before. These rings are made of ice chunks and rock.

NAME: _____

Introduction to the Solar System

1. Circle the word **TRUE** if the statement is TRUE **or** Circle the word **FALSE** if it is FALSE.

   a) Planets that are made of gases tend to move more slowly than the smaller, rocky planets.

      TRUE   **FALSE**

   b) Mercury, Venus, Earth and Mars are known as *inner planets* because they have rocks inside them.

      TRUE   **FALSE**

   c) Moons are part of the solar system because they orbit around the Sun.

      TRUE   **FALSE**

   d) The *gas planets* can have rings and often have many moons.

      TRUE   **FALSE**

   e) *Asteroids* are known as "space trash" because they are left over from when the planets were formed.

      TRUE   **FALSE**

   f) The farther a planet is from the Sun, the more difficult it is to visit it.

      TRUE   **FALSE**

   g) The rings around Venus are made of ice and rock.

      TRUE   **FALSE**

   h) The inner planets have few moons around them.

      TRUE   **FALSE**

   i) The Earth is the center of the solar system.

      TRUE   **FALSE**

2. a) ~~Cross out~~ the words that are **NOT** part of the solar system.

   moon   satellite   planet   comet   asteroid   quasar   sun

   b) **Underline** planets that are light and fast.

   Mercury   Venus   Saturn   Jupiter   Mars   Neptune

   c) Circle all of the items in the list that planets can be made of.

   helium   rock   dust   fireballs   hydrogen   oxygen   ice

NAME: _____

Introduction to the Solar System

3. Below is a list of terms that you read in the text. Choose FOUR words that link well together. In your notebook, write a paragraph that uses all four of the terms. Remember that a good paragraph has a topic sentence, main points and a concluding sentence.

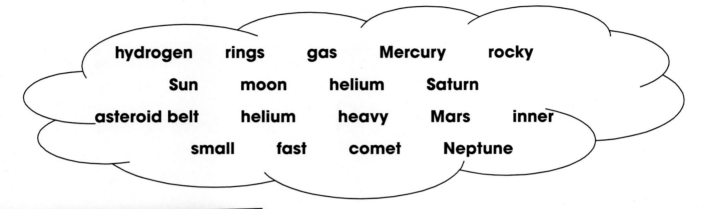

hydrogen   rings   gas   Mercury   rocky

Sun   moon   helium   Saturn

asteroid belt   helium   heavy   Mars   inner

small   fast   comet   Neptune

Research & Extensions

4. The planets of our solar system are classified in many ways: by size, by their composition (what they are made of), and where they are located. You read how location is used to group the planets into inner and outer planets. Use the first T-chart on the next page to compare them.

5. Use the second T-chart on the next page to compare the rocky planets with the gas planets.

6. Use books or other sources to research **two** planets of your choice. Create your own T-chart to record the comparisons that you make as you read.

7. Choose which of the two planets in our solar system would be best to visit, and think about your reasons why. **Design a poster to advertise shuttle trips to that planet.** Your poster should highlight the interesting things that you learned about the planet.

WEB CONNECTION

To learn more about the planets in our solar system, search the Internet using the words "astronomy" and "kids". You can also try to search with the words "solar system" and "kids".

NAME: _____

Comparing Planets Using T-Charts

Inner Planets	Outer Planets

Rocky Planets	Gas Planets

NAME: _____

The Inner Planets

1. In your journal, tell what you know about **Mars**. There have been many missions to Mars in recent years, and you have probably heard a bit about it in the news. At the end of your entry, write **three questions** that you still have about Mars.

2. For each term listed below, find a term from the word bank that would make a **good match** for it. These pairs of words have something in common. Explain the **common link** in the space provided. The first one has been done for you.

clouds	~~Venus~~	oxygen	asteroids	orbits	magnet

		Term from Word Bank	Common Link Between the Terms
	Earth	**Venus**	*These two planets are next to each other and are of similar size.*
a)	rotates		
b)	nitrogen		
c)	gravity		
d)	meteoroids		
e)	atmosphere		

3. State which of the following statements are FACT and which are OPINION.

_____ a) It would be better to live on Venus than on Mercury.

_____ b) Venus has no moons.

_____ c) Humans could live on Mars one day.

_____ d) The clouds around Venus are poisonous.

NAME: _____

 Reading Passage

The Inner Planets

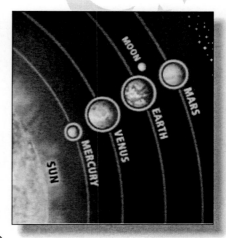

The eight planets of our solar system are organized into **inner planets** and **outer planets**. The inner planets are the first four planets from the Sun: Mercury, Venus, Earth and Mars. They are rocky planets. An **asteroid belt** divides the inner planets from the outer planets.

Mercury is the planet closest to the Sun. It has a very weak **atmosphere**, which means it has very little air. There is no water on Mercury. It has many deep scars on its surface from huge **meteorites** that crashed into it more than three billion years ago. On Mercury, the days are very hot and the nights are very cold. Mercury has no moons. Scientists do not think there can be life on Mercury.

Venus is the second planet from the Sun, and it is the brightest planet. You could not live on Venus because there is a layer of thick, yellowish clouds around it. These are not like the clouds we have on Earth. They are poisonous clouds made of **sulfuric acid**. Both days and nights are very hot on Venus, and it is very windy there. There does not seem to be any water on Venus. Nothing lives on Venus. Venus has no moons. It is often called Earth's "**twin planet**" because it is almost the same size as Earth, and it is next to Earth. Venus is also very different from Earth in many ways.

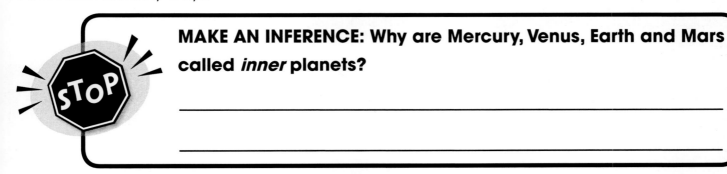

MAKE AN INFERENCE: Why are Mercury, Venus, Earth and Mars called *inner* planets?

_____

_____

Earth is the third planet from the Sun. It has everything that living things need: sunlight, water, and certain gases. Earth has an **atmosphere** made up of mostly **nitrogen** and **oxygen**. It also has a **magnetic field** all around it that comes from the core of the Earth. The magnetic field acts like a magnet and pulls everything in. This keeps you from floating away! You may know this as **gravity**. The magnetic field also works with the atmosphere to protect us from the deadly rays of the Sun. The Earth spins around, or **rotates**, the Sun like the other planets. It makes a full rotation every twenty-four hours. This means that almost every part of the Earth has a night and a day. The Earth has one moon that **orbits** (circles around) it, called Luna. Earth supports many different life forms, like humans, animals, plants, and bacteria.

The Inner Planets

Mars is the fourth planet from the Sun. It has nights and days much like Earth. It also has clouds, fog, volcanoes, and canyons, like Earth. Mars is often called the **"Red Planet"** because its soil is red. Mars has sand dunes, boulders and rocks. Mars also has many craters. Scientists think there used to be large, deep lakes on Mars, but there is no liquid water there now. Mars has two tiny moons orbiting it. There is a possibility that there might be life on Mars.

In 2003, NASA sent two **Mars Exploration Rovers** (think of high-tech dune buggies) to the planet to search for water. They are called Spirit and Opportunity. These rovers were left on Mars. Scientists on Earth drive them around like remote control cars to learn about the planet. They take great photos of the planet and send them back to Earth for us to see. The rovers helped scientists find **evidence** to prove that there might have once been water on Mars. There are **channels** all over Mars that look like they could be dried up riverbeds. The only water present today is frozen in polar ice caps on Mars.

With no water on Mars, very cold temperatures and severe dust storms, it would be very difficult for humans to live there. Scientists say that we would have to live underground, or in domed areas to protect us. Plus, we would have to find a way to get oxygen and water from the icy soil. In other words, we are a long way away from sending people to live there.

WEB CONNECTION

To learn more about the missions to Mars, and see actual photos taken by the Mars Exploration Rovers, search "NASA" on the Internet.

NAME: _____

The Inner Planets

1. **Circle** the word **TRUE** if the statement is TRUE **or** **Circle** the word **FALSE** if it is FALSE.

   a) Mercury has enough air and water to support life.
       TRUE   **FALSE**

   b) Venus is called Earth's "twin planet" because they have the same number of moons.
       TRUE   **FALSE**

   c) A magnetic field is needed on Earth to create gravity.
       TRUE   **FALSE**

   d) The Earth rotates while it orbits the Sun.
       TRUE   **FALSE**

   e) Mars is called the "Red Planet" because of the glare from the Sun.
       TRUE   **FALSE**

   f) Mars has more things in common with Earth than Venus does.
       TRUE   **FALSE**

   g) Scientists think there was probably water on Mars long ago.
       TRUE   **FALSE**

   h) The discovery of "channels" on Mars proved there was never any water on Mars.
       TRUE   **FALSE**

   i) Astronauts explored Mars by driving around in Rovers.
       TRUE   **FALSE**

2. Write each term beside its meaning. A dictionary may be used, but try to use 'context clues' first to find the meaning.

atmosphere	meteorites	asteroid belt	sulfuric acid
gravity	magnetic field	rotates	orbits

   _____ a) a poisonous, deadly gas

   _____ b) spins around on an axis

   _____ c) lumps of rock from space

   _____ d) a pull that holds things together

   _____ e) the air surrounding the Earth

   _____ f) circles around an object

   _____ g) works with the atmosphere to protect Earth from the sun's rays

   _____ h) thousands of rocks that form a band between the inner and outer planets

The Inner Planets

3. You have read some comparisons about Venus and Earth. In your notebook, create a Venn Diagram to show the similarities and differences between these two planets. Set your Venn Diagram up like this:

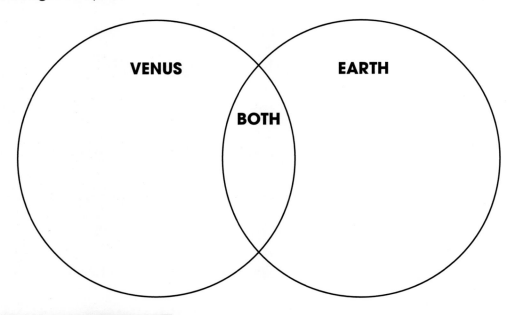

Research & Extensions

4. When NASA landed a shuttle on Mars in its 2005 mission, it was just the next step in a series of missions that came before it. The missions to Mars have occurred in three stages: **flybys, orbiters,** and most recently, **landers** and **rovers.**

a) Research all the International missions to Mars and **create a timeline** to show the progress made toward landing there. Classify each mission you list as one of the terms given above. Use the Timeline Organizer on the next page to record your findings.

b) The Mars Exploration Rovers (MER) are used to explore the surface of Mars. Research the MER to see how its **design** relates to its **function**. Draw a sketch of the rover, including labels to identify its main parts.

c) NASA believes that future missions to Mars might include sub-surface exploration (looking below the ground) to study the planet's geology. **Design a transportation vehicle** that might be used for this purpose. Include a detailed sketch with labels. You may wish to research photos of the Mars Exploration Rovers as an example of a surface-exploring vehicle.

Timeline Organizer

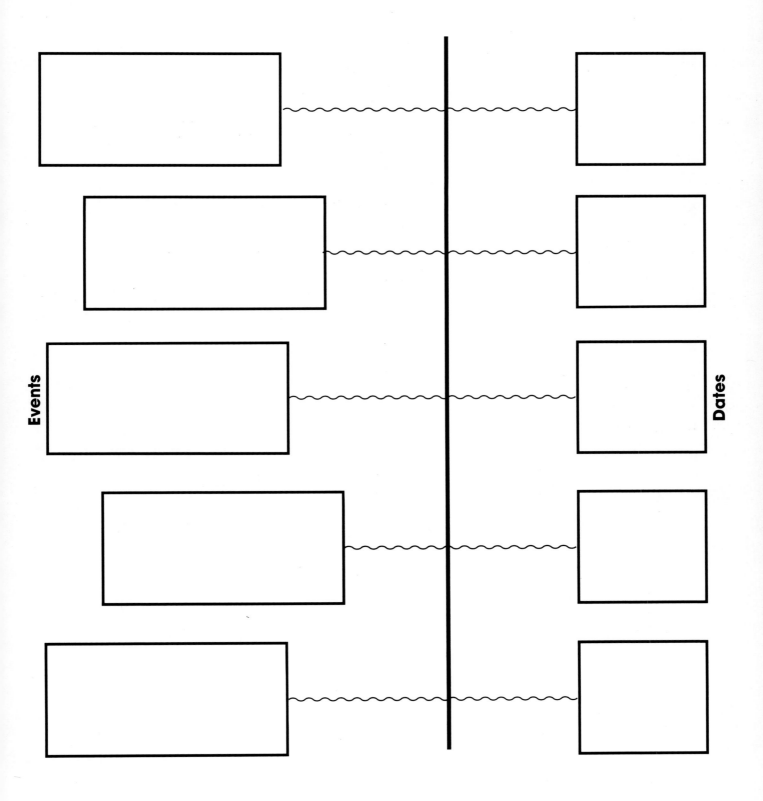

Events

Dates

NAME: _____

The Outer Planets

1. Pluto used to be considered an outside planet but has since lost its status. What do you know about this? Do you have an opinion on it? Write a response in your notebook that answers these questions. Make some predictions about the reason why Pluto is no longer classified as a planet any more.

2. For each of the words listed below, find a synonym from the word bank. Remember that a synonym is a word that has the same meaning.

   a) zone _____

   b) belt _____

   c) giant _____

   d) gas _____

   e) dwarf _____

   f) orbit _____

   g) rotate _____

   h) geyser _____

   i) spot _____

   ### Word Bank

little	area
band	spin
hoop	encircle
vapor	mark
huge	spring

3. Label the diagrams below with terms from the following list:

rotate	orbit	ring	spot

   a) _____ **b)** _____ **c)** _____ **d)** _____

The Outer Planets

Unlike the inner planets, the outer planets are made of gas. They are lighter, they move fast and most of them are larger than the inner planets. The outer planets are: **Jupiter, Saturn, Uranus,** and **Neptune**.

If you were traveling from the Sun to the other end of the solar system, you would first pass the four inner planets. Then, you would go through the **asteroid belt** in the large space that divides the inner and outer planets. The first of the outer planets that you would come across is Jupiter.

Jupiter is the fifth planet from the Sun and the largest planet in the solar system. It is so big that more than one thousand Earths could fit inside it! You would not be able to land on Jupiter because it is a **gas giant**, which means it is almost entirely made of gas. You may recognize Jupiter because of its large **red spot** and the wide bands around it. Fast-moving clouds surround Jupiter to form the wide bands called **zones** and the narrow bands called **belts**. Scientists think that the red spot in one of the zones is probably a huge gas storm that has lasted for hundreds of years. This storm is three times the size of our planet Earth. Jupiter has rings, active volcanoes, lightning bolts and at least sixty-three known moons.

Visualize: Based on what you have just read about Jupiter, draw a sketch of this planet in your notebook. Include as much detail as possible and neat labels. You may need to re-read the paragraph for more detail.

Saturn is the sixth planet from the Sun. It is also a gas giant, but it is best known for it's brilliant **rings**. The rings around Saturn are made of chunks of rock, ice and dust. Scientists think that rings form around a planet when objects get too close. The planet's gravity pulls them into **orbit** around the planet. The actual planet has a striped appearance like Jupiter. The stripes are swirling clouds. Saturn also has at least sixty-two known moons! One of the moons, Titan, is the largest moon in the solar system.

The Outer Planets

Uranus was just discovered about 200 years ago. A scientist was looking through a telescope and spotted the gas planet. Uranus looks blue-green because of the **methane gas** in the atmosphere. It has faint gray rings around it and at least twenty-seven known moons. Uranus **rotates** (spins) differently than the other planets. It spins as though it is lying on its side. Scientists thought another planet's gravity might be pulling it to spin like that. They looked for another planet that might be doing this and found Neptune! This is how the next planet in our solar system was discovered.

Neptune is the eighth planet from the Sun. It is also a gas giant. It is a very cold planet, and it is very far away. It takes twelve years to get there! Neptune is also a blue-green planet, like Uranus, but it is very stormy. Neptune has at least thirteen known moons. One of the moons, Triton, has many geysers. **Geysers** are springs that shoot up super-heated vapors (gases) constantly.

The four gas giants that you have just read about are similar in many ways. They are made of gas, they are very large, and they have many moons and rings. **Pluto** used to be considered the last of the outer planets, but it just didn't seem to fit in! First, Pluto is tiny. It is the smallest planet in the universe. Second, Pluto has just three moons. The largest one is named Charon. It's only a bit smaller than Pluto, so some scientists called Pluto and Charon **"double planets"**. (Earth and its moon, Luna, are also known as double planets because their sizes are similar.) The other two moons, Xena and Ceres, were just discovered in 2005. Finally, Pluto is made of ice and rock, unlike the gas giants.

On August 24th, 2006, scientists re-classified Pluto as a **"dwarf planet"**, which means it can no longer be counted with the other eight planets. Poor Pluto lost its planetary status! As far as we know, Pluto is the end of the solar system. Scientists agree that there could be a lot more to discover beyond Pluto that we just haven't seen yet. After all, Pluto was only discovered in 1930. Who knows what might be discovered next! In 2006, NASA launched the **New Horizons** spacecraft, set to fly by Pluto and Charon.

After You Read

The Outer Planets

1. Put a check mark (✓) next to the answer that is most correct.

a) Which TWO planets have the most known moons orbiting it?

○ **A** Neptune
○ **B** Saturn
○ **C** Jupiter
○ **D** Earth

b) Which of the outer planets is the largest?

○ **A** Neptune
○ **B** Uranus
○ **C** Jupiter
○ **D** Saturn

c) What are Saturn's rings made of?

○ **A** rock and ice
○ **B** dust
○ **C** meteorites
○ **D** 'a' and 'b'

d) Why would Pluto be colder than all of the other planets?

○ **A** It is so small.
○ **B** It is made out of ice.
○ **C** It is not a real planet.
○ **D** It is farthest from the Sun.

e) Which of the following is a true comparison of Pluto and the other outer planets?

○ **A** Pluto is not made of gas like the other giants.
○ **B** Pluto has rings like Uranus.
○ **C** Pluto is around the same size as the other giants.
○ **D** Pluto is warmer than Jupiter.

f) Why are the Earth and Luna known as "double planets"?

○ **A** They are both made of rocky material.
○ **B** They both orbit the Sun.
○ **C** They are of similar size.
○ **D** Earth's moon is actually a planet.

The Outer Planets

Answer each question with a complete sentence.

2. What causes Uranus to rotate on its side?

_____

_____

3. What do scientists believe is the cause of the red spot on Jupiter?

_____

_____

4. How do scientists think the rings around Saturn were formed?

_____

_____

Research & Extensions

5. The gas giants are so different than Pluto that it's not surprising people have asked if Pluto should even be considered a planet at all. There was great debate from scientists around the world before it finally lost its planetary status in 2006. Create a T-chart in your notebook to outline the case for Pluto to lose its planetary status. On the other side of the chart, outline the case for Pluto to remain as a planet. You may need to research some points. When you are done, pretend you are a lawyer who is arguing for or against Pluto. Write an argument that you would deliver to a judge in court to state your case.

6. Create a **comic book hero** based on each of the four gas planets, and their small friend, Pluto. Include as much detail as you can about each planet in their superhero persona. (For example, Nasty Neptune may be able to ward off her opponents with her steamy geysers.) Illustrate each superhero, and give a description of their powers written below.

7. Research the New Horizons mission to see it's path. Create a timeline of it's travels.

WEB CONNECTION
To learn more about the New Horizons mission to the end of the solar system, visit the NASA Missions web page at: www.nasa.gov/mission_pages/newhorizons/main/index.html

NAME: _____

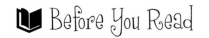

The Moon

1. Some people think that a full moon is bad luck. Why do you think that is? Write about the **superstitions** surrounding full moons in your notebook.

2. **Use a straight line to match each term with its meaning.**

lunar	**A**	One part of a series of steps
phase	**B**	A period of time when a repeating pattern is completed once
cycle	**C**	A bowl-shaped cavity or pit
calendar	**D**	A table that shows the days, weeks and months of a year
reflect	**E**	To throw back light, heat or sound
crater	**F**	Relating to the Moon

3. **Write the diagram number that best fits each term below.**

_____ **a)** full moon

_____ **b)** new moon

_____ **c)** first quarter moon

_____ **d)** last quarter moon

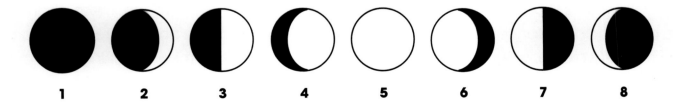

1   2   3   4   5   6   7   8

NAME: _____

The Moon

The Earth has one moon. It is called **Luna**. There is no air, water or life on the moon. There are a lot of rocks and **craters**. Craters are big holes in the surface of the moon. They were formed when big **meteorites** crashed into the moon millions of years ago. The moon's **gravity** is not as strong as the gravity on Earth, so you could jump really high on the moon.

When you look up in the night sky, the largest thing you can see is the moon. That is because the moon is our nearest neighbor in space. It is more than 238 800 miles from Earth. It looks like a bright, white ball, but the moon does not actually make its own light. It just **reflects** the light from the Sun. While the Earth orbits the Sun, the moon is orbiting the Earth. It takes the moon twenty-eight days to orbit around the Earth once. This is called a **lunar cycle**.

STOP

MAKE A CONNECTION: Imagine there is less gravity on Earth for one day. List THREE ways that you would make the most of this situation, and give a reason for each one.

_____

_____

You might have wondered why the moon seems to change shape a little bit each night, from a big, bright ball to a tiny sliver, or **crescent**. The moon doesn't actually change shape; it is always round, but sometimes only parts of it are lit up by the Sun. When the moon is round and full, the Sun is shining directly on it. When you can only see a sliver of the moon lit up, the Sun is shining on the backside of it. The moon has days and nights just like the Earth. When the moon looks mostly dark, you are looking at the part that is experiencing night. Look closely and you might still be able to see the dark outline of the rest of the moon. These changes in the moon's appearance are called the **phases** of the moon. The phases are: new moon, half moon (waxing), gibbous moon (waxing), full moon, gibbous moon (waning), half moon (waning), old moon. **Waxing** means growing and **waning** means shrinking. **Gibbous** means swollen on one side. A **lunar calendar** tells people what phase the moon is in every day.

NAME: _____

 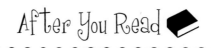

The Moon

1. **Number the events from 1 to 6 in the order that they occur in the lunar cycle. (You may wish to draw sketches to help you.)**

    a) **Last quarter**: The left half of the moon is illuminated.

    b) **Waxing gibbous**: Most of the moon's surface is illuminated except for a small sliver on the left side that remains in the dark. It is almost fully illuminated.

    c) **Full moon**: The entire side of the moon facing the Earth is illuminated. It looks perfectly round.

    d) **New moon**: The side of the moon facing the Earth is not illuminated. We cannot see the moon at this phase.

    e) **First quarter**: The right half of the moon is illuminated. In the next phase, the moon will seem even larger.

    f) **Waning crescent**: Only a small sliver of the moon is still illuminated on the left side. It is just about to "disappear" completely.

2. a) ~~Cross out~~ **the words that are __not__ related to the lunar cycle.**

    waxing   gibbous   gravity   new   crater   crescent

    b) (Circle) **the words that describe conditions on the moon.**

    dry   windy   hot   rocky   bumpy   fiery

    c) __Underline__ **the words that describe what the moon looks like at different phases of its cycle.**

    sliver   crescent   pie   octagonal   orb   star

The Moon

Answer each question with a complete sentence.

3. Why is it that astronauts have **less** weight on the moon than they have on Earth?

_____

_____

4. Describe the positions of the **Earth**, **Sun** and **Moon** when the moon is full.

_____

_____

5. Why is the moon so bright on a clear, cloudless night?

_____

_____

Research & Extensions

6. We say that there is a **new moon** when the moon is between the Earth and the Sun. When this happens, we cannot see the lit side of the Moon, so the moon is dark in the night sky. Another time the moon is dark is when there is a **lunar eclipse**.

a) Research eclipses, and create a model or diagram to show the difference between lunar and solar eclipses.

b) In China, people believed that when there was a lunar eclipse a Dragon had swallowed the Moon. Research this legend, and recount it either as a comic strip, short story or poem.

c) Have you ever heard the expression, "Once in a Blue Moon"? Research **Blue Moons** to see if they actually exist. If they do, explain what they are.

d) Design a model that will effectively teach the phases of the lunar cycle and lunar eclipses.

NAME: _____

The Stars

1. Have you ever star-gazed before? What do you wonder about when you look up at the stars? Write your answers as a reflection journal in your notebook.

2. Complete each sentence with a word from the list. Some words will be left over. You may use a dictionary to help you.

astronomer	**moon**	**astrologist**	**ice**	**Sun**
asteroids	**meteors**	**eons**	**light years**	**constellation**
dust	**microscope**	**telescope**	**navigate**	**North Star**

a) The brightest star in our sky is the _____.

b) Stars begin as balls of gas and _____ that clump together and get bigger and bigger over time.

c) Shooting stars are not actually stars. They are _____.

d) Scientists measure the distance between stars using _____. This is the distance that light travels in one year.

e) A scientist who studies the stars is called an _____.

f) The Hubble space _____ is used to view the stars in the universe.

g) Stars have been used by sailors to _____ the ocean for hundreds of years.

3. Choose **one** of the words from the list below and find out what it means. Then, match it with a word from the word bank that relates to its meaning.

a) _____ nebula

b) _____ supernova

c) _____ galaxy

d) _____ universe

Word Bank
1. explosion
2. cloud
3. whole
4. star system

The Stars

Scientists estimate that there are *trillions* of stars in the universe. You could probably see about 3,000 of them on a clear night if you live in the country. Did you know that stars have a **life cycle**, just like living things? They are born, they grow up, and then they die. A star begins as a cloud of gas and dust, called a **nebula**. As the cloud moves around, it picks up more and more gas and dust. Picture a snowball rolling down a hill and getting bigger and bigger. The star gets really big and hot; eventually it runs out of gas and burns out. The burnt out star will blow up, shrink or go cold. This whole cycle can take billions of years to happen.

Why can people who live in the country see more stars than people who live near a city?

_____

_____

There are many types of stars. The **Sun** is a star called a **yellow dwarf**. It may seem funny to think of the Sun as a "dwarf" because it seems so much bigger than other stars. Did you know that the Sun is actually much smaller than most stars? It just looks bigger because it is closer to the Earth. Except for our Sun, stars are not part of our solar system because they are so far away. They are part of the **universe**.

Blue stars are much bigger than yellow stars, so they are called **blue giants**. They are very bright and very hot. When they die, they grow larger and larger and then explode into a **supernova**. Supernovas are so bright that they can be seen from very far away. There are even bigger stars than blue giants. They are called **super giant stars**. The largest one you can see with your bare eyes is **Betelgeuse**. It is 700 times bigger than the Sun.

NAME: _____

 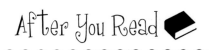

The Stars

1. Fill in each blank with a term from the list. Some terms will be left over.

dies	yellow dwarf	red dwarf	shrink
gas	nebula	black hole	farther
millions	closer	Sun	trillions
supernova	blue star	life cycle	shooting stars

A star begins as a dust and gas cloud, called a _____ **a**, that continues to

pick up more and more dust and gas until it's a burning hot star. As its _____ **b**

continues, the star burns up its _____ **c** until it runs out. When this happens,

the star _____ **d**. After this, the star will explode, _____ **e**, or just

go cold. If the star is an especially large one, like a _____ **f**, it will explode

into a _____ **g** which is bright enough to be seen from very far away. The

_____ **h** is a much smaller star. It is called a _____ **i** star. It just

looks so much bigger to us than other stars because it is _____ **j** to us. There

are _____ **k** of stars in the universe, but we can only see about 3,000 of them

from Earth.

2. Number the events from ①1 to ⑤5 in the order they occur in a star's life cycle.

☐	**a)**	The dust and gas particles in the star continue to get more and more compact, making the star burn hotter and hotter.
☐	**b)**	The nebula continues to gather more and more dust and gas particles.
☐	**c)**	A nebula forms from dust and gas particles in a galaxy.
☐	**d)**	The star blows up, shrinks, or goes cold.
☐	**e)**	The star runs out of gas and burns itself out.

NAME: _____

The Stars

Answer each question with a complete sentence.

3. Why does the Sun seem so much larger than the other stars, when it is actually a great deal smaller?

_____

_____

4. What happens to a star that has died?

_____

_____

5. What is a **supernova**?

_____

_____

Research & Extensions

6. When some super giant stars die, they leave behind a **black hole**. You may have heard of black holes in science fiction novels, video games, movies, or on television shows.

a) Conduct enough research on black holes using print and/or Internet resources to learn **five** interesting points. Record your five points on the Star Organizer on the next page.

b) Organize your five points into a **paragraph** that explains what a black hole is. Remember to start your paragraph with a topic sentence, then add the details and finish with a concluding statement. Use the Organizer on page 32 to help you.

c) Create a comic strip that includes a black hole in the storyline. You will need to think about what kind of action could take place around a black hole, and then create characters and write a plot for your story. Present it as a 3 to 5-section comic strip.

WEB CONNECTION
To learn more about the Hubble Space Telescope, search the Internet using the words "Hubble telescope". See if you can find pictures of what the sky looks like through the Hubble Space Telescope. Also, look for information on how to make your own telescope!

Star Organizer

Black Holes

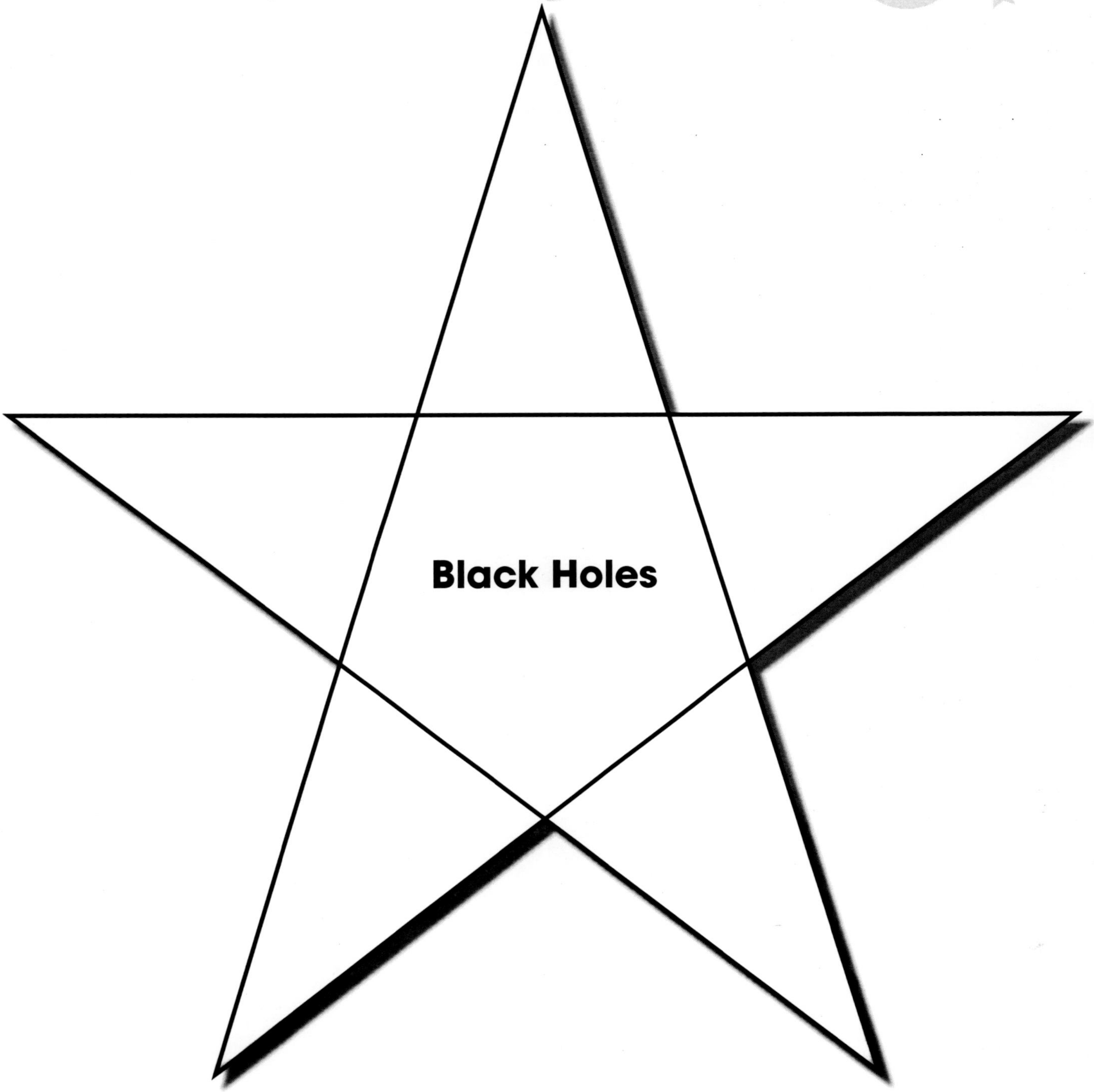

Where did you get your information? (Be specific.)

_____

_____

Paragraph Organizer

Hint: Remember to <u>indent</u> the first word of your paragraph five spaces.

TITLE: _____

Write a TOPIC SENTENCE that tells the reader what you are going to write about.

_____
_____
_____
_____
_____
_____

Include the MAIN POINTS that you will share about your topic. Use 3 to 5 sentences in this main body of the paragraph. It's the biggest part!

_____
_____
_____
_____
_____
_____
_____
_____
_____
_____

Wrap up your paragraph with a CONCLUDING SENTENCE. Do not use the word "I".

_____
_____
_____
_____

NAME: _____

Constellations

1. Have you ever star-gazed at the night sky? What stories have you heard about the patterns the stars make? Write a response in your notebook to tell what you know about the stars.

2. Complete each sentence with a term from the list. Use a dictionary to help you.

navigation	stars	constellation	legends	Big Dipper

   a) Sailors often use the stars in the sky to help them with _____, so they know which way to sail their boats.

   b) A _____ is a group of stars that people have used to form a picture and create a story about.

   c) For centuries people have created _____ to explain how the constellations they see in the sky got there.

   d) One of the most famous groups of stars in the northern hemisphere is the _____. It is part of a larger constellation.

   e) Each constellation is made up of a group of neighboring _____ that form the outline of an imaginary picture.

3. Sketch **three** constellations that you recognize when you look at the night sky. Label them.

   _____   _____   _____

Constellations

For thousands of years, people have gazed up into the night sky and seen pictures of people, animals, gods and other objects in the stars. These "pictures" are not really there, of course, but people imagine them as giant connect-the-dots images made of stars. Great **legends** were made up to go with each of these star pictures. Today, we call a group of stars that make up a picture, a **constellation**. There are 88 recognized constellations.

The most famous constellation is the **Big Dipper**. You have probably seen it before, but did you know that it is not actually a constellation? It is just a small part of the larger constellation known as **Ursa Major** (or Great Bear). The Big Dipper is called an **asterism**. This is an easily recognizable group of stars, but not an official constellation. The Big Dipper is quite useful in helping to find the **North Star**. If you look at the two stars that make up the right edge of the bowl, they are called the **pointer stars**. If you connect them and extend the line north, you will find the North Star. The North Star was used for **navigation** because it is right above the North Pole.

MAKE AN INFERENCE: Why do you think people spent their time making up stories about star patterns in the sky so long ago?

_____

_____

Stories of Ursa Major

The ancient Greeks created a legend that told the story of how the Great Bear ended up in the stars. The great god, Zeus, was in love with Callisto, the river goddess. Zeus' wife, Hera, did not like this very much so she turned Callisto into a bear. Zeus put the big bear into the sky with a little bear, Callisto's son, Arcas. You can see Ursa Major and **Ursa Minor** in the sky still today.

Native Americans believed that the three stars that make up the tail of the bear (or the handle of the Big Dipper) were actually three hunters chasing the Great Bear.

Constellations

1. Put a check mark (✓) next to the answer that is most correct.

a) How were constellations created?

○ **A** The stars were formed into patterns millions of years ago.

○ **B** People imagined pictures in different groups of stars.

○ **C** Stars got pulled into orbit by Earth's gravity.

○ **D** Scientists discovered them using telescopes.

b) How have the old constellation legends been passed to us today?

○ **A** Each time someone made one up, they wrote it down in a big journal.

○ **B** Scientists recorded them on paper centuries ago.

○ **C** People have told them over and over for generations.

○ **D** None of the above.

c) How is the Big Dipper related to Ursa Major?

○ **A** The Big Dipper is a small part of Ursa Major.

○ **B** The Big Dipper points directly at Ursa Major.

○ **C** Ursa Major is part of the Big Dipper.

○ **D** They were both created by the Aboriginal peoples of North America.

d) What must be true of stars for them to be useful in navigation?

○ **A** They have short life-spans.

○ **B** They orbit around the Earth.

○ **C** They help to create good stories when you are bored at sea.

○ **D** They maintain their positions in the sky.

e) Which of the following stories about Ursa Major really happened?

○ **A** A woman was turned into a bear because someone was jealous of her.

○ **B** Three hunters chased a bear.

○ **C** The bear drank from the big dipper when it was thirsty.

○ **D** None of the above.

NAME: _____

Constellations

Answer each question with a complete sentence.

2. How can someone find the North Star?

_____

_____

_____

3. Why would sailors need to use the stars for navigation?

_____

_____

_____

4. Whose story about Ursa Major is correct: the Greeks' or the Native Americans'?

_____

_____

_____

Research & Extensions

For centuries, people have gazed up at the stars and used their imagination to see pictures and tell stories.

5. Research the story of the constellation called **Orion**. Draw a diagram of it, and recount the story as either a comic strip or a poem.

6. Create a **Constellation Slideshow Viewer** using a shoebox, black construction paper for constellation slides and a pin to make the holes. Prepare a description for each of your slides.

7. Use a slideshow-making computer program to create a slideshow of your **five** favorite constellations. For each one, have a slide to show the constellation and one to tell its story.

8. **Create your own constellation** from existing stars and write a legend to go with it.

NAME: _____

Asteroids, Meteors and Comets

1. What do you think a **shooting star** is? In your notebook, describe what you know about how it looks, what it is made of and what it does.

2. Unscramble the words below. You will find all of the words in the word bank, but there are extra ones there, too, that you don't need. When you figure out which word it is, write the correct number from the word bank beside it.

a) _____ ROEADSIT

b) _____ MERTEO

c) _____ CETMO

d) _____ REATRC

e) _____ MORIETEET

f) _____ TEBL

Word Bank

1. SPACE	2. ROCKET
3. COMET	4. MOON
5. ASTEROID	6. METEOR
7. ROCKY	8. METEORITE
9. BELT	10. CRATER

3. Use the six words that you unscrambled above to fill in the blanks from the paragraph below.

There are lots of other things in our solar system besides planets, moons, and the Sun. Between

Mars and Jupiter, there is an _____ _____ . This has many rocks
                                    a   **b**

that are traveling in orbit around the Sun in a wide band. Sometimes one of these rocks will

leave the belt and begin to travel on its own. As it flies through the solar system, it is called a

_____ . When this object crashes into Earth, it is called a _____ .
        c   **d**

It will leave a _____ where it lands. Not all objects are made of rock. A
                       e

_____ is made of dust and ice. The ice melts as it approaches the Sun. The
        f

melting ice-ball looks like it leaves a tail behind it as it goes.

Asteroids, Meteors and Comets

In addition to the planets, Sun and moons that make up our solar system, there are a lot of other objects floating around out there. Some of these objects are asteroids, comets and meteors.

Asteroids are the thousands of rocky lumps that form a circle around the Sun in a big band between Mars and Jupiter. One of the biggest asteroids, **Ceres**, is about 620 miles across. Others are as small as a grain of sand. Several hundred thousand asteroids have been identified so far. Asteroids are leftover rocks from the time when the planets were first formed. The asteroids in the **asteroid belt** never joined in forming the planets because the force of Jupiter's pull kept them where they were. Today, the asteroids continue to remain "stuck" in the asteroid belt.

VISUALIZE: In your notebook, draw a sketch of what you think an asteroid belt looks like in the solar system.

_____

_____

Meteors start off as lumps of rock in the **asteroid belt** between Mars and Jupiter. The rocks break out of the belt and travel on their own. Once they start flying through space, beyond the asteroid belt, they are called meteors. **Meteors** are also known as **shooting stars**. Rocks that are big enough to fly through the Earth's atmosphere and reach the ground without burning up, are called **meteorites**. When a meteorite hits the Earth it leaves a **crater** (or cavity) from the impact. Scientists think that 50 tons of these space rocks hit the Earth's surface every day!

Comets are different than asteroids and meteors because they are made of dust and ice, like dirty ice-balls. They are just a few miles in diameter. Usually, they just circle the outer edge of the solar system. Sometimes a comet is drawn toward the Sun and so it comes hurtling through the solar system. As it travels, it melts and leaves behind a **tail** of gas. This makes the comet look like it has a head and a tail.

After You Read 📖

Asteroids, Meteors and Comets

1. **Number the events from** ☐1 **to** ☐6 **in the order they occur.**

☐ **a)** Meteorites crash into Earth.

☐ **b)** Asteroids orbit the Sun in a wide band, called the asteroid belt.

☐ **c)** Meteors break away from the asteroid belt and fly through the solar system.

☐ **d)** A crater is made on the Earth's surface when a meteorite hits it.

☐ **e)** Leftover space rocks are pulled into orbit by Jupiter.

☐ **f)** The planets are formed, but some rocks are leftover as space trash.

2. ⬭Circle the word **TRUE** if the statement is TRUE **or** ⬭Circle the word **FALSE** if it is FALSE.

a) Shooting stars are made of ice and dust.

    TRUE   **FALSE**

b) The tail of a comet is created by the heat of the Sun.

    TRUE   **FALSE**

c) Asteroids can be as small as a grain of sand or as big as 620 miles across.

    TRUE   **FALSE**

d) You can see asteroids from the Earth without a telescope.

    TRUE   **FALSE**

e) You can see meteorites from the Earth without a telescope.

    TRUE   **FALSE**

f) Comets are made of dust and ice.

    TRUE   **FALSE**

g) Asteroids could have developed into planets if it weren't for Jupiter.

    TRUE   **FALSE**

h) Asteroids leave a tail of gas behind them as they fly through the solar system.

    TRUE   **FALSE**

i) Comets are more similar to asteroids than meteors are.

    TRUE   **FALSE**

NAME: _____

Asteroids, Meteors and Comets

Answer each question with a complete sentence.

3. Why do comets appear to have tails?

_____

_____

4. What is the difference between a **meteor** and a **meteorite**?

_____

_____

5. Why do some people call asteroids, meteors and comets "space trash" or debris?

_____

_____

Research & Extensions

6. Sometimes comets and meteors can put on quite a show as seen from Earth. These can be remarkable events to witness because they are not very common. Other times, our close encounters with this "space trash" can be more dangerous, like when a meteorite hits the Earth.

a) Research **meteor showers**. Try to find out what they look like and what causes them. Prepare a **slideshow presentation** on the computer that informs about this event. Include information about when the next meteor shower is expected to occur.

b) Comets can be quite a spectacle to see as they race across the sky. Research **Halley's Comet** or another famous comet. **Create a poster** that advertises a chance to see the comet on its next trip near Earth.

c) Hundreds of meteors hit Earth each year, but they rarely create any significant damage. There have been times when large meteorites have caused great destruction upon impact. Research some cases of **disastrous meteorite impacts**. Make notes from your research by recording the most interesting points you find.

Graph It!

You read a great deal of information about each of the planets in our solar system. This is an opportunity to sort out what you know. Look back in the book to fill in all of the blanks on the table below:

PLANET CHART

PLANET	Position from the Sun	Inner or Outer?	Rocky or Gas?	# of Moons	# of Rings	Other interesting feature
	1					
	2					
	3					
	4					
	5					
	6					
	7					
	8					

When you have completed this task, re-create this table on a poster board to display in your classroom. Make your poster attractive so that others will want to read it. Consider adding a Visual Representation column for a drawing or photo of each planet.

You will need:

- poster-sized paper or bristol board
- a long ruler for making lines in table
- markers

Build It!

SOLAR SYSTEM MODEL

Create a model of the solar system that shows all of the planets in relation to the Sun, according to their size and position. There are a few ways that you can do this.

1) Create a diorama - Paint the inside of a shoebox black and stand it on its side. Make planets using plasticine and hang them with thread from the top of the box.

2) Create a mobile - Use a cardboard circle as a base for your mobile. Paint Styrofoam balls to represent the planets, and then hang them through cut-out circles in the base.

3) Create a model - Use straws or skewers to connect painted Styrofoam balls at appropriate distances from each other.

4) Your own idea

Prepare an oral presentation on your model to deliver to the class for your presentation.

Build It!

CONSTELLATION SLIDESHOW

You will create a three-slide presentation for your class that will tell the story of three different constellations of your choice.

You will need:

* pictures of constellations to choose from
* dark, heavy paper
* a hole punch or other tool for punching holes in paper
* a flashlight or light source (an overhead projector may be used)
* a dark projection area

Steps

STEP ONE: Select the star constellation that you will use.

STEP TWO: Draw the constellation on dark, heavy paper and punch (or cut) out the stars when you are finished.

STEP THREE: Test your slide using a flashlight to ensure the holes are large enough to let ample light through.

STEP FOUR: Repeat steps 1-3 twice to create three final slides.

STEP FIVE: Research the three constellations to write a brief summary of the stories assigned to them.

STEP SIX: Rehearse your slideshow, with slides and stories together.

STEP SEVEN: Present the slideshow to the class.

If time permits, you may create additional slides for your presentation.

 Hands-On Activity # 4

Try It!

SIZE AND DISTANCE OF THE PLANETS

You will use the attached templates to create a scale model of a solar system.

Steps

STEP ONE: Color and cut out the planets on the sheet provided.

STEP TWO: Stand at one end of a hallway, or large space or outdoors. Mark this point as the Sun.

STEP THREE: Place the Earth 22.4 inches from the Sun.

STEP FOUR: Without looking at the table below, place the rest of the planets at the distance you think they are from the Sun.

STEP FIVE: Check the table to measure the actual distances between the Sun and each of the planets. Place your planets at the correct distances.

PLANET	Distance to the Sun (mi)	Distance to the Sun (in)	Distance to the Sun (ft)
Mercury	35 983 610	8.7	0.7
Venus	67 232 360	16.2	1.3
Earth	92 957 100	22.4	1.9
Mars	141 635 300	34.0	2.8
Jupiter	483 632 000	116.3	9.7
Saturn	888 188 000	213.6	17.8
Uranus	1 783 950 000	429.1	35.8
Neptune	2 798 842 000	673.2	56.1

Note: If you wanted to include a model of the Sun using this scale, it would have to have a diameter of 0.208 inches.

Casting Call

Each of the eight planets in the solar system has its own unique traits just like the characters in a book, movie or video game do. Use what you know about the planets to turn each one into a superhero character. You will have to create the name, look and personality of each planetary figure. Use the chart below to help organize your work.

Planet	Superhero Traits	Superhero Name	Superhero Sketch
Mercury			
Venus			
Earth			
Mars			
Jupiter			
Saturn			
Uranus			
Neptune			

Then, you can choose one of the following activities to do:

1: Design a comic strip that tells a story using your characters. (Perhaps the inner and outer planets face-off in a battle for solar system domination!)

2: If you were going to make a movie based on your superheroes, which Hollywood stars would you cast in each role and why? Use photos from the internet to make your cast.

3: Write a story about your Superhero crew. It could tell about a mission they must complete together, or it could tell the story of how their smallest member (Pluto) was kicked out of the crew.

Crossword Puzzle!

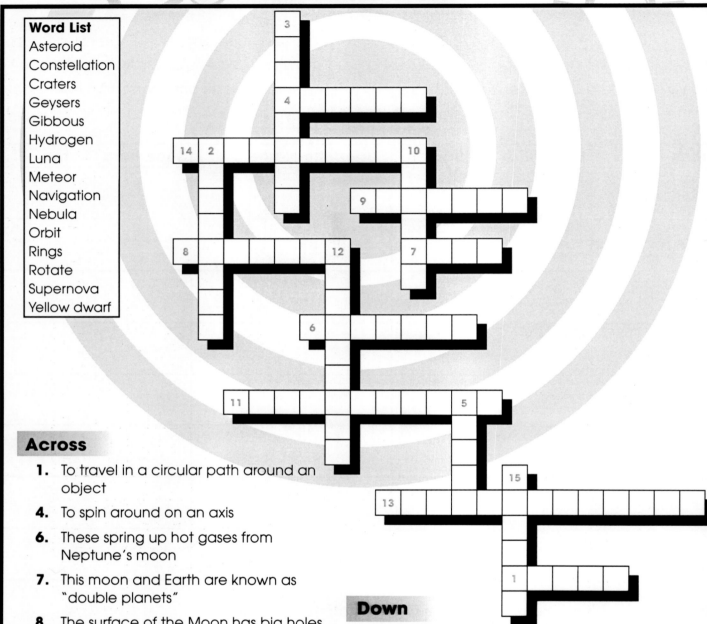

Word List
- Asteroid
- Constellation
- Craters
- Geysers
- Gibbous
- Hydrogen
- Luna
- Meteor
- Navigation
- Nebula
- Orbit
- Rings
- Rotate
- Supernova
- Yellow dwarf

Across

1. To travel in a circular path around an object

4. To spin around on an axis

6. These spring up hot gases from Neptune's moon

7. This moon and Earth are known as "double planets"

8. The surface of the Moon has big holes called _____

9. This is one of the phases of the lunar cycle

11. The Sun is known as this type of star (2 words)

13. A group of stars that make up a picture

14. Stars can be used to help humans with _____

Down

2. A piece of space rock that orbits the Sun

3. One of the gases that the gas planets are made of

5. Saturn is surrounded by _____ made of rock, dust and ice

10. The birth place of a star

12. A star explosion

15. This is also known as a shooting star

Word Search

Find all of the words in the Word Search. Words are written horizontally, vertically, diagonally, and some are even written backwards.

MERCURY	MOON	RINGS	TELESCOPE
NEPTUNE	METEORITE	SATURN	CRATER
COMET	MARS	CONSTELLATION	YELLOW DWARF
VENUS	ECLIPSE	ORBIT	GRAVITY
PLUTO	SOLAR SYSTEM	URANUS	MAGNETIC FIELD
METEOR	JUPITER	ASTEROID	GEYSERS
EARTH	STARS	ROTATE	CRESCENT

```
T N E C S E R C M Z X C V B N M A S
Q W E R T Y U Y E L L O W D W A R F
Z S X C V B N S T A R S M A S D F G
W Q U E R G T Y E U I G O P A S D N
D Z X N S R D F O G H N J K Q W R E
L A S D E A F G R H J I K L A U S P
E Z X C V V B N J G A R A S T D F T
I A S D F I R H J Q S W E A R T Y U
F Z S W X T O R B I T A S Z M O O N
C S D J F Y T G H J E K L W E E R E
I A Z U X C A D F G R C N Z T X C V
T Q W P L U T O Z X O O C V S V D F
E C L I P S E A S D I M F G Y Z X C
N Z X T C V B N M T D E Q W S E R T
G X S E S N M X A T J T L P R L G M
A C V R M N K L O U Y R C R A T E R
M Z A S D M L F G H J K L Q L W E R
Z X C V B E A S T E L E S C O P E Y
S A D F T R G H J U R A N U S L Q W
Z X C S A C S G E Y S E R S D F S X
C V N B N U A S D F G H J K L Z R X
Q O E T I R O E T E M S F H T R A E
C S W E R Y T Y U I O D G Q W E M K
```

NAME: _____

Part A

Comprehension Quiz

35

Circle the word **TRUE** if the statement is TRUE **or** Circle the word **FALSE** if it is FALSE.

8

1. The planets in our solar system are classified as rocky or gas planets.

   TRUE   **FALSE**

2. In our solar system, all eight planets orbit the Sun.

   TRUE   **FALSE**

3. The inner and outer planets are divided by a *meteor shower.*

   TRUE   **FALSE**

4. Earth has one moon, and the other planets have many moons or no moons at all.

   TRUE   **FALSE**

5. The Sun is just one of many stars in our solar system.

   TRUE   **FALSE**

6. The moon has many phases that are tracked on a lunar calendar.

   TRUE   **FALSE**

7. When an asteroid hits the Earth it forms a crater in the surface.

   TRUE   **FALSE**

8. Scientists believe they may be able to send humans to live on Venus one day.

   TRUE   **FALSE**

Part B   **1. Label the diagram by filling in the blanks below.**

8

A _____
B _____
C _____
D _____
E _____
F _____
G _____
H _____

A

3

2. Use the diagram above to answer the questions.

a) If you were to include the asteroid belt in the diagram, between which two letters would it go? _____ and _____

b) With which letter would a geyser be placed? _____

c) With which letter would Luna be placed? _____

SUBTOTAL: **/19**

After You Read 📖

Comprehension Quiz

Part C

Answer the questions in complete sentences.

1. Outline the life cycle of a star.

4

_____

_____

_____

2. Explain why Pluto lost its planetary status and was reduced to a **dwarf planet**.

3

_____

_____

_____

3. Which planet is known as Earth's **twin planet** and why?

3

_____

_____

_____

4. Identify and describe the **three** forms an asteroid can take.

3

_____

_____

_____

5. Give **three** ways that a comet differs from an asteroid.

3

_____

_____

_____

SUBTOTAL: /16

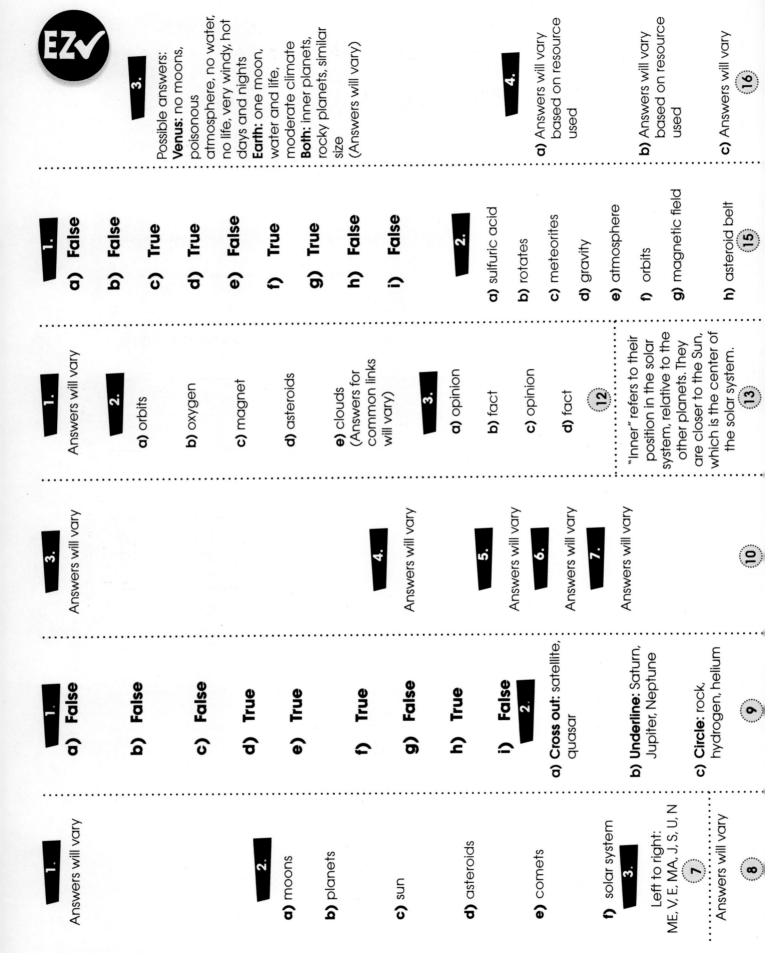

EZ✓

3.

Possible answers:
Venus: no moons, poisonous atmosphere, no water, no life, very windy, hot days and nights
Earth: one moon, water and life, moderate climate
Both: inner planets, rocky planets, similar size
(Answers will vary)

4.
a) Answers will vary based on resource used
b) Answers will vary based on resource used
c) Answers will vary

(16)

1.
a) False
b) False
c) True
d) True
e) False
f) True
g) True
h) False
i) False

2.
a) sulfuric acid
b) rotates
c) meteorites
d) gravity
e) atmosphere
f) orbits
g) magnetic field
h) asteroid belt

(15)

1. Answers will vary

2.
a) orbits
b) oxygen
c) magnet
d) asteroids
e) clouds
(Answers for common links will vary)

3.
a) opinion
b) fact
c) opinion
d) fact

(12)

"Inner" refers to their position in the solar system, relative to the other planets. They are closer to the Sun, which is the center of the solar system.

(13)

3. Answers will vary

4. Answers will vary

5. Answers will vary

6. Answers will vary

7. Answers will vary

(10)

1.
a) False
b) False
c) False
d) True
e) True
f) True
g) False
h) True
i) False

2.
a) **Cross out:** satellite, quasar
b) **Underline:** Saturn, Jupiter, Neptune
c) **Circle:** rock, hydrogen, helium

(9)

1. Answers will vary

2.
a) moons
b) planets
c) sun
d) asteroids
e) comets
f) solar system

3.
Left to right:
ME, V, E, MA, J, S, U, N

(7)

Answers will vary

(8)

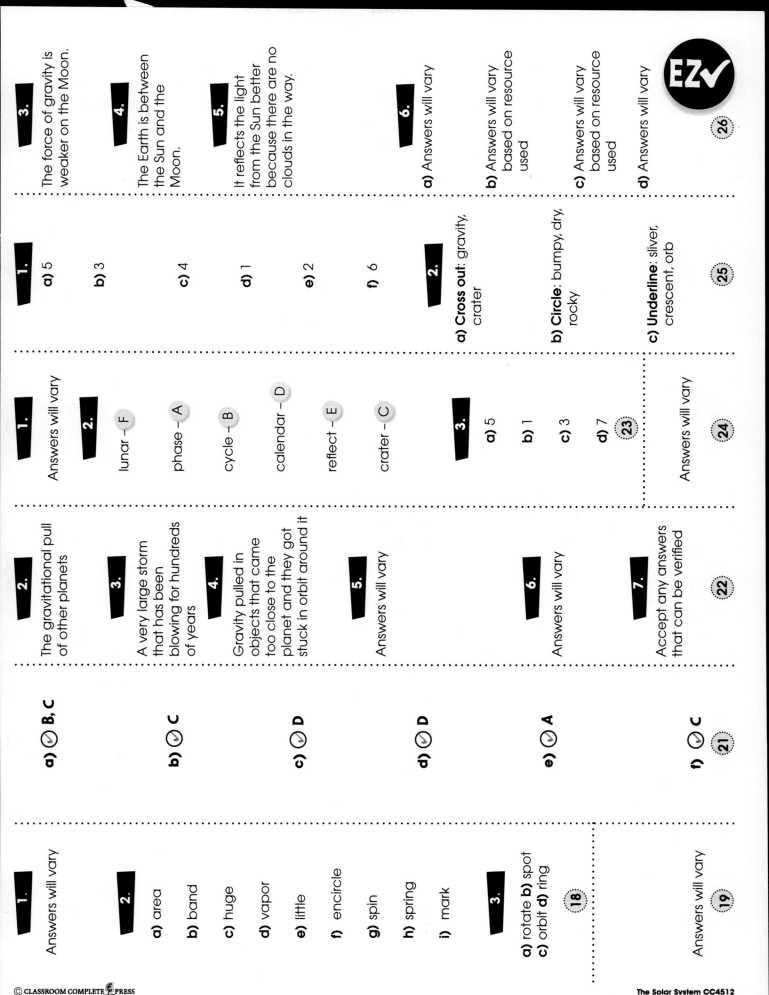

1. Answers will vary

2.
a) area
b) band
c) huge
d) vapor
e) little
f) encircle
g) spin
h) spring
i) mark

3.
a) rotate b) spot
c) orbit d) ring

(18)

Answers will vary

(19)

---

a) ⊘ **B, C**

b) ⊘ **C**

c) ⊘ **D**

d) ⊘ **D**

e) ⊘ **A**

f) ⊘ **C**

(21)

---

2. The gravitational pull of other planets

3. A very large storm that has been blowing for hundreds of years

4. Gravity pulled in objects that came too close to the planet and they got stuck in orbit around it

5. Answers will vary

6. Answers will vary

7. Accept any answers that can be verified

(22)

---

1. Answers will vary

2.
lunar – F
phase – A
cycle – B
calendar – D
reflect – E
crater – C

3.
a) 5
b) 1
c) 3
d) 7

(23)

Answers will vary

(24)

1.
a) 5
b) 3
c) 4
d) 1
e) 2
f) 6

2.
a) **Cross out**: gravity, crater
b) **Circle**: bumpy, dry, rocky
c) **Underline**: sliver, crescent, orb

(25)

---

3. The force of gravity is weaker on the Moon.

4. The Earth is between the Sun and the Moon.

5. It reflects the light from the Sun better because there are no clouds in the way.

6.
a) Answers will vary
b) Answers will vary based on resource used
c) Answers will vary based on resource used
d) Answers will vary

(26)

EZ✔

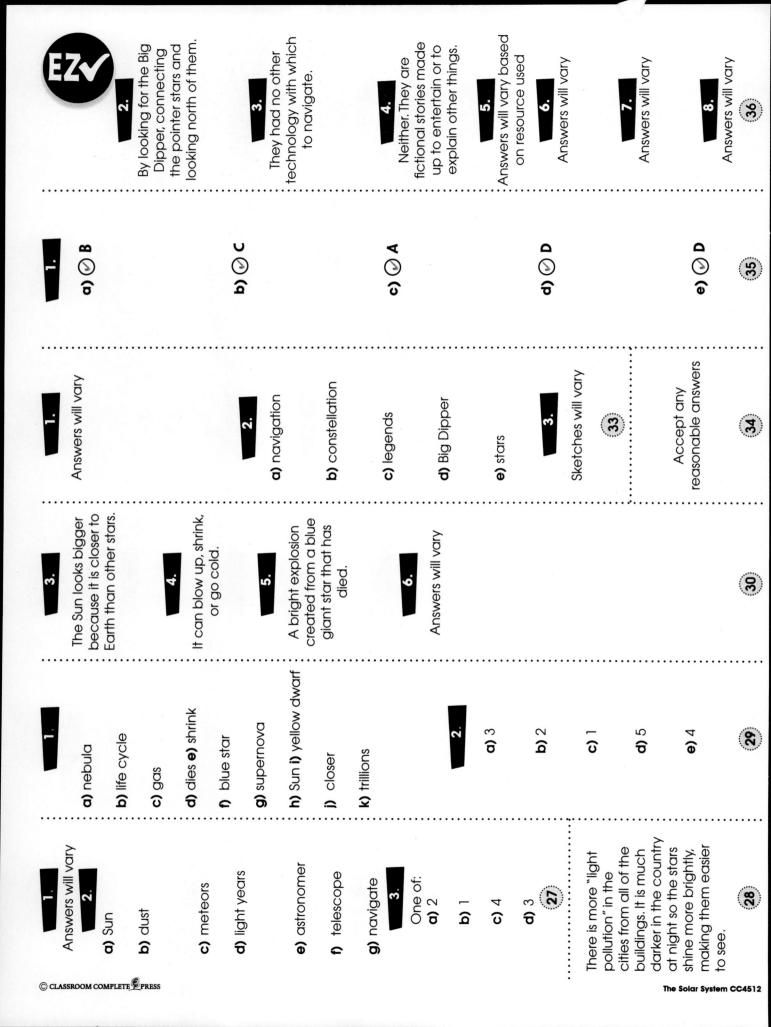

EZ✓

2. By looking for the Big Dipper, connecting the pointer stars and looking north of them.

3. They had no other technology with which to navigate.

4. Neither. They are fictional stories made up to entertain or to explain other things.

5. Answers will vary based on resource used

6. Answers will vary

7. Answers will vary

8. Answers will vary

(36)

1.
a) ✓ B

b) ✓ C

c) ✓ A

d) ✓ D

e) ✓ D

(35)

---

1. Answers will vary

2.
a) navigation

b) constellation

c) legends

d) Big Dipper

e) stars

3. Sketches will vary

(33)

Accept any reasonable answers

(34)

---

3. The Sun looks bigger because it is closer to Earth than other stars.

4. It can blow up, shrink, or go cold.

5. A bright explosion created from a blue giant star that has died.

6. Answers will vary

(30)

1.
a) nebula

b) life cycle

c) gas

d) dies e) shrink

f) blue star

g) supernova

h) Sun i) yellow dwarf

j) closer

k) trillions

2.
a) 3

b) 2

c) 1

d) 5

e) 4

(29)

---

1. Answers will vary

2.
a) Sun

b) dust

c) meteors

d) light years

e) astronomer

f) telescope

g) navigate

3.
One of:
a) 2

b) 1

c) 4

d) 3

(27)

There is more "light pollution" in the cities from all of the buildings. It is much darker in the country at night so the stars shine more brightly, making them easier to see.

(28)

Part C

1. Like people, stars are born, grow up and then die. A star begins as a gas and dust cloud called a nebula that continues to pick up more dust and gas and get bigger and bigger. As it gets larger, it grows hotter and hotter. Eventually it just burns itself out and dies.

2. It doesn't fit in with the other outer gas giants. It is tiny; it is made of rock and ice; it has just three moons, one of which is the same size as it.

3. Venus, because it is almost exactly the same size and it is right next to Earth.

4. An asteroid is a lumpy rock that is held in orbit in a belt between Jupiter and Mars. When an asteroid breaks free of the belt and flies through place on its own, it is called a meteor. If the meteor flies through the Earth's atmosphere without burning up, it's called a meteorite.

5. A comet is made of dust and ice. It is usually located on the outer edge of the solar system, and when it flies through space it leaves a tail of gas behind.

49

Part A

1) True
2) True
3) False
4) True
5) False
6) True
7) False
8) False

Part B

1.
A Neptune
B Uranus
C Saturn
D Jupiter
E Mars
F Earth
G Venus
H Mercury

2.
a) D,E
b) A
c) F

48

Across

1. Orbit
4. Rotate
6. Geysers
7. Luna
8. Craters
9. Gibbous
11. Yellow dwarf
13. Constellation
14. Navigation

Down

2. Asteroid
3. Hydrogen
5. Rings
10. Nebula
12. Supernova
15. Meteor

46

3. They leave behind a tail of gas as they get closer to the Sun and start to melt.

4. They are the same object but are called different things depending on where they are.

5. They are all leftover objects that float around in space (lumps of rock, dust balls, ice chunks, etc.).

6.
a) Accept any answers that can be verified
b) Answers will vary
c) Answers will vary based on resources used

40

1.
a) 5
b) 3
c) 4
d) 6
e) 2
f) 1

2.
a) False
b) True
c) True
d) False
e) True
f) True
g) True
h) False
i) False

39

1. Answers will vary

2.
a) 5
b) 6
c) 3
d) 10
e) 8
f) 9

3.
a) asteroid b) belt
c) meteor d) meteorite
e) crater
f) comet

37

Answers will vary

38

Word Search Answers

T	N	E	C	S	E	R	C	M	Z	X	C	V	B	N	M	A	S		
Q	W	E	R	T	Y	U	Y	E	L	L	O	W	D	W	A	R	F		
Z	S	X	C	V	B	N	S	T	A	R	S	M	A	S	D	F	G		
W	Q	U	E	R	G	T	Y	E	U	I	G	O	P	A	S	D	N		
D	Z	X	N	S	R	D	F	O	G	H	N	J	K	Q	W	R	E		
L	A	S	D	E	A	F	G	R	H	J	I	K	L	A	U	S	P		
E	Z	X	C	V	V	B	N	J	G	A	R	A	S	T	D	F	T		
I	A	S	D	F	I	R	H	J	Q	S	W	E	A	R	T	Y	U		
F	Z	S	W	X	T	O	R	B	I	T	A	S	Z	M	O	O	N		
C	S	D	J	F	Y	T	G	H	J	E	K	L	W	E	E	R	E		
I	A	Z	U	X	C	A	D	F	G	R	C	N	Z	T	X	C	V		
T	Q	W	P	L	U	T	O	Z	X	O	O	C	V	S	V	D	F		
E	C	L	I	P	S	E	A	S	D	I	M	F	G	Y	Z	X	C		
N	Z	X	T	C	V	B	N	M	T	D	E	Q	W	S	E	R	T		
G	X	S	E	S	N	M	X	A	T	J	T	L	P	R	L	G	M		
A	C	V	R	M	N	K	L	O	U	Y	R	C	R	A	T	E	R		
M	Z	A	S	D	M	L	F	G	H	J	K	L	Q	L	W	E	R		
Z	X	C	V	B	E	A	S	T	E	L	E	S	C	O	P	E	Y		
S	A	D	F	T	R	G	H	J	U	R	A	N	U	S	L	Q	W		
Z	X	C	S	A	C	S	G	E	Y	S	E	R	S	D	F	S	X		
C	V	N	B	N	U	A	S	D	F	G	H	J	K	L	Z	R	X		
Q	O	E	T	I	R	O	E	T	E	M	S	F	H	T	R	A	E		
C	S	W	E	R	Y	T	Y	U	I	O	D	G	Q	W	E	M	K		

47

The Solar System CC4512

Phases of the Moon

Earth

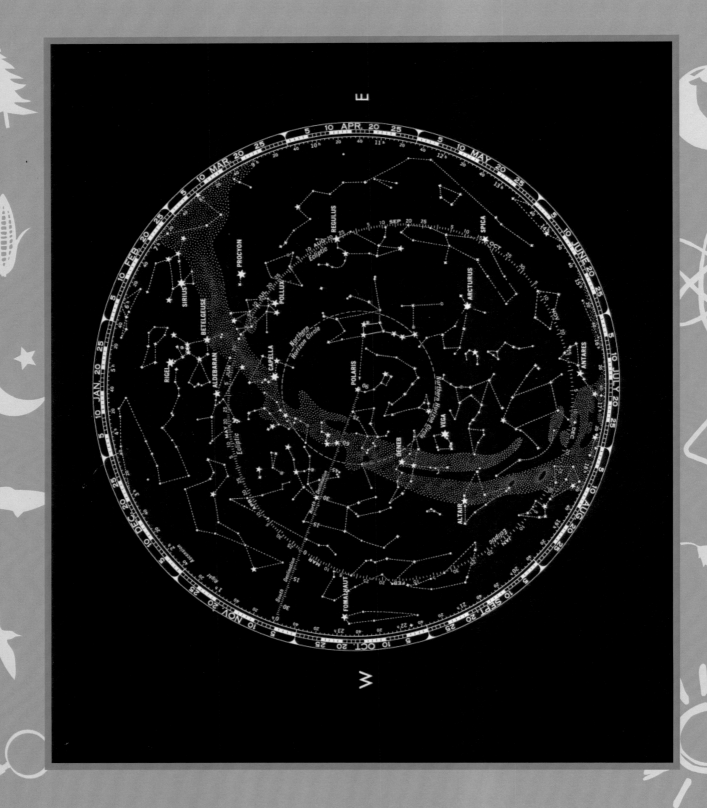